WRITING PLACES

ANTHOLOGY

Navigation

Some cities make excellent pen-pals. Kolkata and Norwich have over fifteen hundred years of literary history between them. Despite enormous differences, literature is each city's shared and defining art form and provides the cultural and historical thread that runs through the histories of their city regions, communities, and identities. Writing Places is a creative writing and literary translation project exploring the connections between writing and place in Kolkata and Norwich; and this book is the product of a subsequent partnership between the National Centre for Writing, the University of East Anglia, UEA Publishing Project, and Jadavpur University.

Happily for me, many of the Writing Places exchanges happened in real time and space, so I was lucky enough to be one of the writers invited to Kolkata to take part in several collaborations, including the inspiring Literary Translation Winter School at Jadavpur University, and a creative writing workshop with Rimi Chatterjee and the fantastic Jadavpur literature students. The energy of these events naturally suggested further exchange, so with the help of Kate Griffin at the National Centre for Writing, Writing Places Online was born. Writers and translators from both cities were invited to meet virtually to share cities and literary cultures, together mapping a mobile city of the imagination where the Wensum flows with barely a ripple into the Hooghly, where Kalighat and Norwich Cathedral face each other across a mysterious, shifting cityscape, where saints and goddesses and local legends lurk around every corner, where new acquaintances walk and talk under the shade of the willow and the banyan.

The creative energy of live workshops is one thing; the dynamic of online exchange and collaboration is slower and more meditative, perhaps more conducive to exploration. What better way to begin a project that is, in many ways, an alternative guide-book, an anthology of secret maps. The poet Roy Fisher once said of his home-town, 'the city is what I think with,' and this is what participants were invited to do, not just in writing, but through actual fieldwork, and the discovery of what so often goes unnoticed or unrecorded close to home. A certain quality of attention can make one a stranger even to one's own city, and writers were encouraged to explore forgotten histories, personal cartography, folklore and memory as much as the familiar vicissitudes of 21tst century urban life. Each piece of work here is therefore a translation of some sort, in some cases between languages, but also between continents, time-frames, and experiences. And though these stories and poems are as vivid as any documentary account of place, they also have the shimmer of strangeness that is so often the hallmark of good literary writing, in which language responds not just to the insistence of the present, but to the oblique currents of influence and desire, haunting and prophecy. When, after all, are we ever exactly where, and who, we think we are? Perhaps we are all strangers. We are a community of strangers.

Tiffany Atkinson
University of East Anglia,
13 September 2019

By the Wensum: Norwich

RACHEL GOODMAN

It flows for swan
home carrier
of white feather shows
the sky the same crossed high
with gull and contrail cries
of wharf quay gate and mill
fisher friar calling down
from brick-faced balconies where
barges hauled their corn and silk
and Norman stone was hoisted up the hill

it flows with bells
that called in Strangers
and their bright canaries
bobbing under bridges in the flood
rows of willows with spring licks
of yellow down their trailing arms
stroke the surface weeded
with the prayers of Julian who told us
sin is necessary but all shall be well and all
shall be well and every kind of thing shall be

well. It flows
without repentance throwing
over shoulder a song
of something soon made far
while clouds stay constant in its face
and a brown fish twitches underneath.
With a flicker and a spiral fall
a leaf lands unresisted on the river's skin
which with the merest shrug goes on
for swan and sky and spire.

Old Town Serpents

BISHNUPRIYA CHOWDHURI

Like fossils of prehistoric serpents,
these long houses lay.
You cannot tell if they are dead or asleep—
these people in our town
gnarl brick by brick, water drip on wall-skins—blue hues and dentures,
loose in the plastic box by the bed,
you cannot tell if they are asleep or dead.

They jump from the wheat mill and the coughing buses and old generator
machine and fall over photo studios, tea shops, and fritter corners nobody
named like a ghostly muslin.
Rosy numbers from Bollywood dreams dance around the gullies and
the rooftops, their sequined skirts crooning heartaches and love-burns, a
hundred years old
"bina payal ke hi baaje ghungroo..." in the ears of half eaten fish-heads and
unsold goat-heads. Can you hear the lovers kiss and the cooker whistle high
with its belly full of Sunday mutton curry? People walk secretly dazed in
this thickness. Their eyes and ears look alert (except for the droopy wrinkles
and loose skin one can only occasionally see in the bathroom mirror). Their
hands and feet perch firmly on the handles and pedals and they appreciate
good chow mein and biriyani every once in a while. Their tongues lick at
their televisions, the talent shows and operas about well-dressed lives of
troubled human beings. In the complex cartography of their intestine a small
yellow pill of sleep remains undigested. You cannot really tell if they are dead
or asleep. Like an overgrown overripe grapefruit stale rice—lots of stale rice,
bones licked and their chocolatey marrow sucked clean (the bone is a flute
for the leftover soul of a goat and a hungry tongue), imperishable plates from
ceremonies of all kinds burst over the vat and spill. Odorous dahlias bloom
and sway, they heavy the air here and there. Drains ooze and like always it
takes a day's downpour to turn alleys into creeks, unloved and thin. Filth
floats about like stray cats and fishes everywhere. These long houses—their
serpently bellies soak in the flood water, gurgling songs only the deaf can
hear. If you look at their darkish length – their yellow eyes through the
water, you will see the soft quivers, the heavings of a strange dyno creature...

You will see those chalky blue ceilings inside their cavity ribbed with years of life lived and left. Dogs of the town have heard the stories from their mother's mother. Stories of the pale and blue humans who conjured the serpent houses a long long time ago. The river was then alive, curls of her saffron hair carried them on huge ships to the banks of this town and that. Their turquoise irises twinkled like strange magic blossoms as they built rooms and stairways and patios and sometimes pale fingers curled around black coiffures, thick walls hid the butterflies and such secrets were locked between windows and wall shelves and backdoors of all kinds. You cannot really tell if they are dead or asleep. Centuries have passed, families cut and sewn back together and still the spells work, blue eyed babies appear now and then from inside brown wombs when they do serpently laughs are heard collapsing another wall somewhere in those houses of our town.

Dance

RUPSA NAG

The flames licked up a graying azure,
(quite like the grey of your veil)
and moist eyes.
I stood and smelled
your burnt flesh.

They told me smoke creates shapes in the air.
But no, it was you, looking down from the windows.

No one believed, but I knew
as I jumped in and burnt too.

Waltzing in a charred carnival,
They saw us in the smoke.

Who would They now make believe,
that it was us and not ghosts.

The Boy Without a Name

MARZIA RAHMAN

Here, at the road-side café, tea is served by an eight-year-old boy.
He is a refugee.

He is known around as the tea boy, a fond term mostly used by customers.

Among his friends, he's earned the title of lattu master for his mastery
over spinning a top at one go. It's his master whose approach is somewhat
different. Every now and then he comes up with a new name. Maybe it's due
to his old age memory loss. Or maybe he feels it redundant to sustain the
acquaintance for long.

The real name the boy can't recall. It doesn't pester him much, forgetting it.
It's his village name that he regrets not remembering. He'd return there one
day. That's the plan! His heart yearns for his home by the river, flecked by
bamboo groves. In that home, in that village, lived his father, mother, two
sisters, a toddler brother, and a very old grandmother. He had a red truck toy
with a policeman inside that he misses the most.

Now, wearing faded undershirt and grubby trousers, he runs from one table
to another — reeking of cigarettes, cheap scents, and sentiments and serves
hot steaming tea with toast and snacks. It's his job to serve and later collect
the trays of discarded food and drink.

The later part he favors more. As there'd always be tiny tidbits of snacks,
crusts of bread or crumbles of biscuits left for him to relish. He'd polish off
the food fast and lick the tea cups clean. Once in a while, if he's in real luck,
there'd be much left, the customer leaving hastily for reasons unknown.

When he doesn't have work, he sits on a high stool beside the counter and
snoozes. Sometimes he goes to his village, in his dream. The army people
would distribute chocolates and happiness around. They are fine people
whom the villagers are not scared of. In his dream, he waves at them, holding
his little brother in one hand and the red truck in the other, standing in front
of his home by the river, flecked by bamboo groves.

Sometimes, he goes to his house where his very old grandmother grins with toothless mouth, his mother cooks beef curry with potatoes and eggplants on a big stove. The aroma wafts over his senses in waves. He waits for someone to call him. He needs to know his name, and the name of the village, too.

He'd return there one day. That's the plan.

The plan seems flawed. And his returning to his old life a long way off.

Nine hundred nine dreams away. Meanwhile, he serves tea and toast, swings a top and snoozes sitting on a high stool. Waiting for a perfect dream.

Waiting for the name to float.

But as it happens—with most people most of the time in most of the dreams—it shatters. And always, he'd wake up before he gets to the point of knowing it.

———

Anchorage
LILI COOPER

I wear a habit
I am a creature
of coiled up springs
the bed
that straightens too
easily as the
clock's hand
pierces the minutes
like Romans
whose arrows
skewer the target
of pins through palms
in sewing
I am a habit
a creature of Myself
I crawl under
like a toddler
through the
tears in the world's blanket
tracing Myself
like charcoal
making a border
to define a hem
that cannot be felt
but trails long
like losing
my will
I am of habit
routinely rummaging
for my wallet
in a bag of never
ending coins
jingling down the road
like popcorn
breaks its shell

against the stainless steel lid
a regular pattern
of sounds
donating coins
I light a candle
to follow custom
as I am made of habit
I run my finger
under the trail of fabric
like water unquestionably
there today as still it will
be tomorrow
running down
like a shiver
running down
into the lines
that crave
my body
like the arrow
which craves
piercing or burning
a fingertip
haloed in heat
I am a habit
carving itself
like wood
into folds of skin
tightening the
strings so there
are scars that run
like unproductive
worms between my thighs
where the sun
doesn't reach
like the movement

of food down
the gullet of a hen
or geese
I remember being young
holding a hen in my arms
a mother
and feeling the place
where the corn waits
to be digested
like a bag of rice
feeling the way meat feels
under a layer of plastic
partially concealed
like frosted glass
I am a habit
that used to prod the chicken
in supermarkets as a child
wondering why
their flesh is also called
goose pimpled underneath
when they are chickens
I forget how
a creature of habit becomes less
a child more
a chicken of feeding
and laying and breathing and praying
I lay down in bed
covering my head
with a duvet
with the habit
of a day
wondering whether
I am a woman
or children
or a chicken

under a film
of plastic
or habit
beneath the pattern
a living saint
indeed dead.

―――――

We Meet Our Ghosts at Unexpected Street Corners

SUROJIT KAYAL

—Why don't you come a little closer? I don't like to be alone on a date, you know.

We were walking for about an hour now. Just like this—she up front, me following. With very little words passing between us. We were wading through a stranded city desperately honking and swimming along in yellow lights into nowhere particular—through smells of fast food and calls of shop attendants—billboards and hoardings—foreign brands—local politicians—Messi and Ronaldo—an absence of any wind blowing and sweat forming bubbles at our lopsided bodies, until we finally came upon this half-lit, half-deserted street that somehow stood out of time, and she asked me to come up closer.

I could see why. I had taken a little while to adjust to the marked difference of this street from the rest of the city and had fallen behind. The intervals between the lights were longer here allowing the shadows to come in and the street to disappear into the foggy darkness beyond. Staring at one of the yellow lights, right above my head, I had the familiar feeling that I had been to this place before—this has happened before—this street, this light, this walk, this woman before me—I had lived this entire evening before. There was a stir in my memories, I could hear a faint knocking at the gates, and I had an extremely hazy view of things to come as if through an eyehole from the outside. Not much. Hardly anything. Something was trying to come out of something, I knew what it was, though I could not tell at the moment, but I would surely recognise it when it arrived. I was at the same time eager to know and a little afraid of what might be coming.

Her voice brought me out of the reverie. I came up and took her hand. I shot a sideways glance at her to check whether she was the girlfriend I knew or someone else from the distant past. The little face with long flowing hair that I was so fond of playing with coming up to the waist. She was not the most beautiful woman on earth but she was the world to me, a world that was rapidly breaking up and going out of our hands. We were desperately trying to tape it over with these silent dates. Where are we going? I asked and instantly regretted. I could not break the code. This was not an evening to ask questions. Especially at this place. Each word is a stain upon the silence, a crack upon the earth. She did not answer, anyway. Did not even look at me. She just kept walking. I decided to ask no further questions and keep following.

All this while the knocking in my head would continue. In fact, it was growing louder at a very slow pace. I turned my attention inwards a few times and tried to look through the eyehole. Nothing showed itself. But another thought began to grow in me now. That I would never return from this part of the city. That I will be walking with this very woman in these shadowy alleyways of Dee market till my death. And I had taken this upon myself not unaware but in full knowledge. I had cut myself off from my job, my parents, my home on the other side of the city forever in full knowledge.

After some more walking we took a left turn to face a huge enclosure of wired fences and thick trees. There was a very small gate in the middle through which we crept in and walked on dry leaves that rustled beneath our feet up to a gigantic lake. The lake was placid, well cemented, and fenced with steel railings on all sides. Along the banks there were cemented benches on which sat couples of all ages. The railings also had small colourful lights that glowed in the dark but did not illuminate the surroundings. The little faint light that filled the air came from two massive searchlights in two corners of the lake. Beyond them, in the distance, black skyscrapers silhouetted themselves against the dark canvas of the night sky. Looking back I saw the outgrowth of trees was actually planted and well maintained. And from somewhere in the distance came slow instrumental music filling the place. It sounded like a Japanese lullaby, like small drops of water falling upon the petals of a flower floating in the air losing themselves into nothingness forever. In fact, this whole place seemed to me a piece of Japan. The chained waters, the trimmed forest, the dripping music! We stood against the railing close to the water, staring at the lights dancing in the current. It is good in here, I said at one point and regretted again. After a long silence as if from another universe came an answer. Yes.

Some time passed. A long time passed. Two security men with torchlights had already come up to us and politely asked us to leave. After a point, the music too stopped. I looked around and found the couples had all left. We stayed. As the silence deepened I became conscious of other presences all around us. We were not alone. We were being watched. With carefully maintained silence and utmost patience. I could sense the eyes in the trees behind us, the ears turned towards us just below the surface of the water, a very fine breath in the air all around us. They knew something was going to happen soon. Something was actually happening. The knocking in my head grew more intense and the memory was slowly unfurling itself to a point of recognition. I could see what was happening now. I could connect the dots travelling back and forth in time. The sense of living this evening before came back to me in full force. Soon the air grew tense, the water stopped flowing, the invisible creatures held their breath in watchful anticipation. My ears were all warmed up now, my vision blurred into fragmentary images. The knocking had turned into a hammering, the memory a dazzling painting in my head which I could take no further and simply blurted it out, out of myself, speaking and observing at the same time,

—So this is it then.

—Yes. This is it.

A prompt reply. As if she was waiting for it.

—But does it have to be?

Now she turned towards me, came closer, clutched at my shirt on the right chest with her long fingers as she used to do in the early days, and looked into my eyes with all the pensiveness of the world,

—Come on, Su. We have been through this already. Many times. Don't put me through the trial again.

—Yes. I am sorry.

I was genuinely sorry. I should have done better.

—But at least let me accompany you home. It's already late.

—That's all right. I know my way around here. You take care.

And that was it. You take care. Followed by a peck on the cheek and she melted into the darkness without looking back. As she left the water started flowing again, the air became lighter, the invisible creatures relaxed. Their job was done. What was to happen did happen. They were afraid something out of the ordinary would disrupt the course of events. But they could breathe easy now. I came back a few steps from the water and sat on a bench, thinking, unthinking. My nerves calmed down slowly. The knocking had already stopped.

After some more time the two searchlights went off.

———

Consistency

TRANSLATION BY MARZIA RAHMAN

The wild boar will find the dear mud,
The kingfisher will get the desired fish,
The dark nights will turn white in dripping rain,
The peacocks will show its dance in dense forest.

The lover will be united with his beloved, for sure
But they will get no peace, no peace, no peace.

The lone traveler will return to his home,
At the bottom of an empty vessel, the white rice will simmer like a galaxy of stars,
The long-lost lyrics of some old song will find its way to
your voice.

The lover will be united with his beloved, for sure
But they will get no peace, no peace, no peace.

The marches will end in barracks after barracks,
The hungry tiger will find the blue bull,
The breezes in village after village will bring the sweet sound of
some girls singing—And you two will find your place in an abode.

The lover will be united with his beloved, for sure
But they will get no peace, no peace, no peace.

ORIGINALLY BY SHAHEED QUADERI

Moonlit

REBECCA PHILLIPS

cough into your hands; cough out your inhibitions and the sword stuck in your throat. wipe your germed hand onto your poor excuse for trousers, they're damp and stained from hanging out in the back alley anyway. it won't make a difference.

all there is to bathe in is a single strip of light emanating from a street lamp and when that peters out, you're left with the moonlight that doesn't reach you. solely incandescent; the glow you're desperate to touch and desperate to forget.

when the streetlamp finally flickers out, out of gas and out of life, curl your fingers up into the moonlight and grasp the beams between your grip until even your nails have a silver-white tint. like you're the source of the light now, in control of the night and the darkness, directing the tides without seeing them. like you have control over your heart; you've reigned it in and chained it up; it's not going to go wandering where it's not supposed to, like it used to do.

close your eyes into the light. the moon is calling you; the voice clear, alive, and warm, and straining to reach you, not like the empty carcass of the streetlamp filled with falsities and the work of man. the whispered words patch up the holes inside of you like a plaster in the shape of a puzzle piece. no one's going to tear them out this time.

"When we migrate, we murder from our lives those we leave behind."

BISHNUPRIYA CHOWDHURI

We don't murder them. They do us. If you are like me, if you have left the town at night, if you have left the town thirsty to your quivering lips for the new world and happy like a kitten to finally have severed this cord that tied you for so awful long to this soil, not soil, soil is too pristine and full of the purity of the womb... your town pit is aged bricks and haunted debris and rotten potato skins everywhere and soggy newspapers ooze, ooze and conspire to take over every gully, road, street, if you are like me, if you left with two suitcases full of only the nicest clothes and a few books of poetry, if you thought "this was it", this was how you untie yourself from the walls and bicycles, your mother and the old English teacher—his face bobbing up and down the shades of darkness, this is how you forget your father's reading glasses on the table, the asthmatic breath of your grandmother and all those viridian paints on the doors, you have hardly left.

If you are like me, if you thought walking forward, walking as you look only at the gilded horizon of good dreams (those are rare but happen to you often so you believe them almost) was the way to leave, to shed the old skin, painted pretty and strange so many times for the stage performances, to act and dance to the tunes you thought could never stick to you (you have always been so poor in remembering songs), you thought you were okay to lose some friends and the handsome boy who whispered desperately how much he liked you, you thought you will turn your back and walk away and words will lose you, loves and phone calls will lose you, the last words before the dead tone returned into the land-line veins will not come muttering after you through the throaty evenings, you have not left long enough.

If you are like me, if you have crossed oceans and whales, if you have cut your hair, if you have learned to paint your lips and eyes to match the color of your jeans and frocks and trained your tongues to tut-tut-tut to the 'other' language, you will have visitors line up behind your doors. Unlike how you read in the stories, doors will not open to serene beaches or gardens, instead the old English teacher will be waiting, his fingers cold and firm around the red book of English grammar. He will ask you the definition of an adverbial, the spelling of nightingale, you will write nightingale till your spine fluttered and the master vanished. If you are like me you will hum school prayer songs and in those dreams you will be twelve and you will be thirteen and you will be bleeding through your blue-school skirts like dark country maps, stains would swell on your blue school skirts.

If you are like me, they will, they will catch up and greet you with "Merry Christmas!" The debris of your rejected town, debris from space, debris stardust and men. Their faces will glow—the girls and boys, the men and women like fireflies and pickle jars and of course the winged river through the evening. If you are like me, chatter will flow from above the trees, the cackles after the poorest jokes will rise from beneath the ground, calluses— benign brass bells will jingle in your blood and there inside the mirror will be your face, painted thick and strange for the annual dance performance, school performance, recital, and weddings.

If you are like me, they will, oh they will kill you slow, as far as you go

They will kill you slow

———

The Slow Turn of Water

SRISHTI DUTTA CHOWDHURY

the man reaches the ground, lowered in
waves. a hollow grave holds no
desire for the dead. every seed tinged in pomegranate crimson.
from between his legs, the
organ of slow demise. she felt its waft from
over the ground. bowing down, the hands only
reach the chest of grass. the
desire for hair in earth, soft, sometimes
fluid. I know the shape of hard.
skeletal. their boat drowns in
gentle gyration.
the wind has sung this dirge already. you
can write loss in this—the plump, the firm kind.
another centre merges perfectly into the margins, a slow
dive.

The Tourist

MEGHOMALA BHATTACHARYA

One of these days, memory will rebel
and indecision wage war standing upright
in the crowds at Sealdah Railway Station;
for by waving your hands you'd painted me this city
and in the story of your life, my tourist's adventure

bewildered, in the bangla beckoning dubiety at Bara bazaar.
Suddenly you'd lied, you know,
the tripping trams
and traffic jams
and at the signals musical scams,
the metro rail
and Alipore Jail
a bit unlike your fairytale
at Central Park
conservative remarks
my red attire made the street dogs bark.

Now, at the end of three days straight
I look around but your city is gone,
a dead evaporation like the soul that flies
and flees when chased by an endless dream.

This city is the remains of poetry books
an eccentric constellation suffering half mist, half sunshine
a history commencing and killed off by intelligentsia,
a madman's quest, and a tourist's utopia.

Black Shuck

REBECCA PHILLIPS

bursts of thunder cloud the skies,
and rain spatters down like needles;
the church door unlocked, a welcome for the wise
and an invitation for evils.

with every flash darkness follows,
deafening the silent wishes and prayers,
and even the words, the storm swallows;
they weep for a god who cares.

bang, the door's open,
the dark chokes like soot,
count to five, count to ten,
there's something underfoot.

a howl hollows out the room,
and eyes, the shade of a wasp's body,
illuminate; a guided route to the tomb,
"spare us, hear our plea!"

no answer, just claws on wood,
and cries from a frightened child,
will there be a saviour, like He said there always would?
or will the night turn us wild?

Not Meant to Be, 2018
Body on the Floor

KATARZYNA BIELA

My biological clock has its hands all over the place now. Or perhaps they are dangling somewhere around 6 and 8, miserably.

I've been coming to the Sainsbury Centre for Visual Arts every day for the past two weeks. I arrive at 8:55 and, as I enter, I approach the space on the left, in front of the glass wall. I stand in the middle and look outside—it's become my habit now. Spring is in full bloom, so usually, despite the early hour, I can spot a few individuals sank in the grass with a book or a cup of coffee hidden between the leaves and their legs.

I take a breath and feel the smell of dust coming from books, clothes, sheets of paper, and empty packs of crisps around me. I arranged them in a chaotic way exactly thirteen days ago and haven't dusted them ever since. The smell is not too bad. Seems quite cosy and matches the art gallery, especially sculptures from, like, 800 BC - AD 800 or so. The kind of cubical sculptures that are supposed to resemble people.

I might ask someone if I could clean my stuff at some point, but they will probably send me to the coordinator, that is the official and down-to-earth part of myself.

At around 8:58 I look right at the tables in the café—that's become a habit I sometimes wish I hadn't got into. I picture you and your eyes naturally drawn to the sky outside because of the colour match. I see you raising a cup of coffee, the milky flower leaving one of its petals on your lips. And myself raising my hands as if to tie up my hair, only to remind myself that I left the hairband at home and allow the hair to fall down again.

The waitress who cleans the tables always interrupts the image at 8:59 and that's when I step into the mess, close my eyes and lie down with my hands and legs strewn around the cold floor.

I hear shoes walking around and spoons being put on plates for about an hour. Sometimes I have an impression that I hear unfavourable glances, too. Strange comments for sure: "Is she ok?"

"Look! She's really lying here!"

My favourite so far was probably the one shouted by a little girl who must have been standing at the top of the spiral stairs as her voice was definitely coming from afar: "Dad! Is this a real person?"

I try to change my position every now and then, when I assume there is no one around apart from your ghost, but I tend to fall asleep by 10:00. That's when I catch up on resting, leaving you alone at our table for the next eight hours.

———

Almost Human

RUPSA NAG

If I asked you today—
Go up,
to the iron tip of the Cathedral to wave your love one last goodbye,
as I watch you through a bottle which broke after my last supper,
and now it cannot hold wine—
Would you?
I have had nothing to offer since when you stopped talking to me.
Uninspired, you came every day.
Confessed at dumb wood, sang prayers to wax melting away along with your glory.
I thought we could start afresh, over wine but am left with a broken bottle on a
window pane.
I am more human now than you have ever tried to be.
I thought I was lonely up here.
But I see you are the forsaken one, even in cheerful crowds of your own kind.
Why did you go down the streets cursing children under your breath for being a colour akin
to the beautiful soil that nourishes trees heavier than your own being?
You cursed a man on the bus for having eyes too small?
Well, at least they are bigger than the (w)hole of your heart.
If I asked you today, would you want me to see you wave your love one last goodbye?
Would you stand on the iron tip of your inglorious Cathedral, gather the melted wax of faith
fragrant with the dumb wood of confessions
to tell me, you have hated me all along?
To tell me the only sin you ever committed was towards yourself. That of unloving?
Standing tall on the towering iron tip of your Cathedral,
drunk on the wine from your last supper
as the sun pierced your eyes making them so small that you can barely open them,
sweat beads glistening on your neck choked with the ghosts of your hate
you would burn into the hue you previously cursed.
Would you the maddrunk Godlover, throw at me your broken bottle and bid me
one last goodbye?
Only to realise that you can't stand on an iron tip.
But you wouldn't know,
you stopped asking questions, long, long ago.

Bite the Dust

SRISHTI DUTTA CHOWDHURY

hair curl over the patio in cobwebs. hunch. green snot of grass smother her
gracious neck. easy easy easy.

she waits for the bird taking off. shirt comes in the way, yellow hand-me-
downs. reverse the knowledge of skin. jarred are the edges of night come
to soothe her. eyes dissolve in a pool of digits. all this hair is the cage of her
body. no life in vain, the sky erupting in light over the steeple. this is how to
imagine gentle stroking. deny this picture. how to paint the sound of solemn
in the motion of sermon. she tries again, on the dial tone a young voice dying.
prolong every moment. like the snail slide soft off the small of her inside.

Pulsatilla Vulgaris

ALICE WILLITTS

Cancer grows like the pasqueflower.
Sepal drops sepal
and the most delicate nest
of silvery wolf fur, feint as scar tissue
lips the swollen ovaries, waiting
to take flight.

*

I've walked the shattered limestone hills
among the purple tilt of bells.
I've sighed in the softening wind.

What a year it was
that cancer felt like release
respite even.

Progeny

SYAMANTAKSHOBHAN BASU

In the quiet South Kolkata neighbourhood we lived in when I was little, there was a Krishnachura tree older than the oldest building, sitting squat by the side of the road. Over the years, it had climbed higher than the home of the family of judges adjacent to it, leaves brushing their covered balcony like a fringe on a sullen teenager's face.

Right behind this antique duo of old house and ancient tree was a mental hospital. Every morning as mother and I hurried past the sleeping houses and across the dirty paved compound of the asylum, which we had to go through, we would encounter him. Unfailingly, he turned up at 7:12 am each morning, matted locks falling over eyes we could never see, always moving purposefully towards something in the distance. He would stop at the Krishnachura, and begin a familiar refrain—Tu nahin khayega, tera beta beti khayega. You will starve, but your children will eat. There he was, the lunatic Prophet of our comfortable middle-class neighbourhood, his doomsaying the alarm we all woke up to.

We never knew why he wasn't detained. His presence mocked the hospital, mocked the government, mocked all the paranoid pretences of our civilised society. I ventured to ask Sita, the woman who worked in our home, why it was that he roamed free. She looked at me uncomfortably, saying nothing. Finally, after a little prodding, she told me that he had magical powers. He could see into the future, and could lay curses upon anyone who crossed him. No one knew where he came from or how old he was. He had always been there, as long as anyone could remember. Uttering the same words over and over.

The judge's home was shrouded in grief. Their eldest son had died in a car accident. A hush had descended upon the whole neighbourhood, tragedy creeping uninvited into our lives. The Prophet, however, seemed incensed, rushing to and fro shouting at the top of his compelling voice. Everyone turned away as he approached, shuddering and fearful. I asked Sita why he was so affected. She told me, in a voice barely audible, that the dead man had tried to get him committed. Angered by the uncooperative asylum staff, he had taken it out on the Krishnachura, hiring woodcutters to saw off most of its branches. It was a bad omen, she said. Two bad omens. His infant daughter, now fatherless...

I deliberately walked past him on the road that day. In his frenzy he crashed into me, knocking me forcefully to the pavement. He looked at me straight, and my heart turned to ice. His eyes like limitless gorges bore into my very soul, and I knew. I knew my life was nothing. I knew my body was only flesh. I knew that my sole purpose on this earth was to perpetuate, and then pass away into the anonymity of Time. Thus was misery inherited over generations. *Tu nahin khayega, tera beta beti khayega...*

———

Conquerors
KATARZYNA BIELA

a true conqueror
may be the one well-known
for discovering America
or another way to India

but also
the best
at meandering around stalls at Norwich Market
the most handsome
carrying a kayak around the Lake
or the most sensitive
strolling along the River Wensum's weeping willows

Traces of Thisbe

DAISY FLYNN

murmure minime
the slightest whisper
their love golden threads
of voice through a fissure
—a breaking had to occur
to keep them together—
each one weaving figments of the other
binding their bodies
in mismatched tapestries
she imagines the Babylonian breeze
is his breath on her neck
and he pictures her
flawless
faceless

Pyramus told no one that he dreamt of lions' teeth
splitting luminescent skin
and tearing bodies into limbless limbo
earth so red it's like a sea beneath the sun
that's bearing down upon it
birthing dusk

no one questioned what had happened
when they found the lovers
intermingling at last
her arm woven beneath his leg
and white dress painted red
by mulberries weeping

Homeless
NAINA DEY

They cut down three more trees yesterday
Not even the searing heat could stop them
First they lopped off the rickety branches
Then sawed through the trunks
Two of the trees didn't feel anything
They were dead already
Bone-white, leafless, hideous even in the daytime
Poisoned to make way for a new thoroughfare
Or how could one accommodate the increasing number of cars?

There were two sturdy siris trees
The third was a gulmohar the shape of a woman dancing
It was not dead yet
It clung onto life as its branches clung onto a few leaves
And the crow clung to its nest in hope
At least this tree was not dead

But it was no excuse
When they severed the trunk yesterday
And left it for the yellow truck
Today as the gulmohar trundles away
The lone crow sits atop still in hope.

A Loop

VIJAY KHURANA

As he walked he thought about how cruel the whole thing was. They had arranged to meet at the cathedral gate at 3:45pm. He couldn't help thinking she had suggested such a specific time to show him he was being slotted into her day, like a task she would later cross off a list. Plus, 3:45 was too late for lunch and too early for a drink, so what on earth would they do? He already felt the need to suggest something, to have a plan. This was exactly what she wanted him to feel, he thought. He had never had a plan, and she would never stop punishing him for it.

He supposed they would walk down to the river, past the Cow Tower and the rust-red curve of Jarrold Bridge. They would throw smiling questions at each other like little grenades. How was work and how was Charlotte and how were his brothers? As they passed into the shadow of the courthouse, he would feel an enormous pressure to leave her before she left him, before she looked at the cruel little silver watch on her wrist. So without talking about it he would gently turn them into Whitefriars, and they would walk back to the cathedral, where they would say goodbye. The whole thing seemed predetermined, and he ached with the dreariness of it.

He saw the spire of the cathedral rising above the rooftops and took his phone out. She had not messaged him since that one unpunctuated word, *grand*, after he had confirmed the time. Maybe he could call it off. He could turn around and go back to work. He would message her and apologise, of course—he wouldn't just leave her waiting. He couldn't. The image that came into his head then was so thrilling it made him stop walking: she stood waiting in the darkness of the cathedral gate, a silhouette against the bright light behind her. She paced as though caged, her phone in her hand. She walked from one sandstone pillar to the other, stopping every few moments to look up the hill towards the city, scanning the street for him. And he, invisible, uncontactable, always just about to come around the corner and yet never coming, as though he had vanished from the world.

Wild Love

ALICE DAVIES

Two faces masked behind shallow windows
eyes of scared minds whispering into the darkness
pass this
message into the wind.
It's cold outside but this coat of love is
wrapping them into
a world of flowers,
sprouting between the cracks of the
dried up pavement
this love could never be
paved.
This love could never be
paved into something
so concrete—
it's wild.
But as the eyes of scared minds whisper into the darkness
pass this
message into the wind
they will see.
Their wild love grows out from
beneath the surface but
what is affection
what is love
if not a
beautiful weed?

On the Banks of Teesta

PETER MINJ

On a January winter morning,
The gossamer mist engulfs me.
It carries me away in the cold air,
Above the tiny ever-growing city buildings
And gently lowers me on the banks of Teesta, the mysterious green river.

I see footsteps on the white sands,
Once they were mine,
It's been a long time since I walked on them.

The kids blow balloons and frolic around,
The silvery water gushes past the huge boulders,
My mother warns me not to go into the water,
I am a good boy and I listen to her.

I have always been cautious of the river,
Buses have fallen into it, people washed away never to be found—
Adrenaline pumped teenagers have been drowned by its strong currents
But I never blame Teesta.
We have to respect the power of nature.

I recollect how Teesta's beauty captivated me,
The serpentine contour, the murky green surface,
The forested hills rising on either side of it,
Rocky hills, Strong hills, Old hills.

We jump from rock to rock carefully balancing ourselves,
My curly-haired crush moves deftly on the rocks.
I am rather tentative and worried that I will fall.
I am so in love with her.

We don't have smart phones to take selfies,
We don't need one as we are lost in nature.

I can smell the chicken-masala wafting through the air,
My feet can't stop tapping to the rhythm of the song,
All of us hold hands together and we dance in unison,
Our faces look happy, all smiles, at least for a day,
A day worth the wait,
Picnicking on the banks of Teesta.

The mist disperses as the sun comes out,
I am brought back to the present.
I retain the smiles and the joy,
The times have changed, and picnics are no more regular.
People throng the malls more than the serene riverside.
I stand on the bridge and look down at the green waters,
They flow where they have to as life goes on.

A Letter of Amusement

SOPHIE LANDRIDGE

It is peculiar indeed
to feel like a medieval,
the more and more I proceed
with these cathedrals and monstrosity evils.

Wandering around and around
in that figure of eight,
imagining Tombland town
without Cocina and Bond in your fate.

From a settlement
to a place of amusement,
are playful adults in their element
with their drunken excusements.

Concrete jungles and madness,
where students drink
taking away any stress and sadness,
brewers falling on the extinction brink.

Bunnies bounce and bounce around
to the playlist of a barbeque,
laughter and cheer being drowned
by the beauty of Norwich and all its woo.

From the Draftbox of One Named Thomas Under the Subject 'Letters to Leda'

SUROJIT KAYAL

Arthur was hanging from the noose—the noose that could not take him—his eyes bulging—all colours drawn out of his face—the rope broke—he fell down amidst hammer and nails that were raining from the sky that night—he was grovelling on the green grass asking for mercy. I remember his neck bearing the mark for a long time afterwards. But why can't I remember him, Leda? Where is he now?

One sunny afternoon we kissed on the porch—you and I—it was a beautiful summer day of sea green clouds—and the porch was littered with dead white pigeons—they all had razors stuck in their breasts, and the blood was oozing very slowly out of their wounds—the red against the white against the green—the porch was blooming with roses of death that afternoon—I asked you what they meant—you said dreams. Why were our dreams bloody, Leda? Who put razors into them? What curse were we carrying out?

Then the rain came in the dead of the night—an incessant rain that washed away everything we had—you were sitting there in the middle of the porch in your beautiful red gown—your right hand pressed against your cheek—your face turned forestwards—eyes downwards—they thought you wanted to drench—but I saw your tears hiding in the moonshine and the rain—such pain! Why were you paining, Leda? What happened that night that you had to summon the deluge to hide yourself? Was it the rain that washed me clean that night?

Dearest Leda,
Since my memory loss I have lost the gift of language. And with it the
coherence of my memories. Words fail me. The past reveals itself in dis-
connected images that resist translation. This is why I write these emails to
you everyday. To get back to my ways with words. But you never respond.
Will you respond at least this time?

I found an image in my mailbox a few days back. Glass doors opening onto
an enclosure of bright green grass and the forest beyond threatening to
encroach into the porch. Sent without any explanation or subject matter.
Way back in '92, March 14, 3:23 am. It was from you.

Where was this house, Leda? Was it our summer getaway far off into the
counties? It sparks off memories that won't let me sleep because I cannot
make sense of them. I cannot connect them in time. What came of what
or what came after what! Connect them for me Leda. Please! Without
my memories I am perpetually stuck between the past and the present
that opens onto no future. Just like the image that is neither in the house
nor in the garden. Who took it, Leda? From a treacherous position like
that? Was it me? Does it contain the mystery of my undoing? Tell me
everything Leda. Don't deny me my own story. Don't deny me my own
self. I plead you, moor me back to life.

Love Grows Like a Weed Between Bricks

ALICE WILLITTS

I'm blowing you a coloration of columbines
to say, the sea creeps up on us walking,
on the unsinkable sun, to say, congratulations
on your abortion Mihoko, to say, your eye-sockets
dim around your eyes beloved, to say, hoot, little owl, hoot

to say, not nearly enough use is made of that airy
flower that's little more than a weed
that its morals leave much to be desired,
yet I never tire of saying it's a plant that loves
to get between the cracks

like on April 27th when the bombs fell and I knew
you loved me because you told me so
on St Benedicts Street, where we kissed
at last, to say, the doves will coo tenderly
above the crater where we regret we stood.

WITH THANKS TO VAHNI CAPILDEO, HIROMI ITÔ,
ARIANA REINES, WALLACE STEVENS AND VITA SACKVILLE-WEST.

Fatty Liver

SRISHTI DUTTA CHOWDHURY

1. sour cheese. my twelve month sure dinner on store bought careful bread, foxbrown.
2. when I make the call, july preparations of plump orange, soft gazelle for my table. meal for one, hoping for two. gorge on this hungry.
3. the first night of frost: the hounds are nearing, exposing its bones through the light. touch. the pumpkin wrinkles in soft hairs when I arouse.
4. cook for him once. pomegranate and wild rice for the one with the ruler and rules. wielding the knife like its own end. like haggis rich in its own blood, opening us to its character, the tang of death.
5. I have my guests eat in mourning. remember this flesh, the fish eyes gently blanched in old fat, the grease from gander belly and this. choke on this cocoa from a mother's parched back where her child need cling to her.
6. on a certain date after four dates, he splits open a bottle between palms as I cheer him on. the quiet may not know how to riot. gagging on my dribble, I please with my life.
7. on the kitchen table, the wind turns me lazy and slush. Berry season, blue as ice. spell home in this.
8. a boring disaster girl pours herself onto her first feast, a puddle of mud rice, crooked aubergines in green. some after lunch pounding turn me purple, right colour, temperament holding.
9. frequently they tell me, I am missing from the memory of me like he slashed into my insides for pâte. I was taught the polite thing is to morph this body into vegetable. this, over fritters that exacted mother's thumb.
10. a man worth his salt leaves the body that feasts on itself.
11. what is left. learn to chisel a paring knife from flesh still soft as murky fat fed goose.
12. soft cheese. for the tongue still raw from eating.

The Goddess and the Tramp

NAINA DEY

The nameless tree stood cringing
Under the molten sun
Its thick leaves white with dust
The ground burns
Singeing the goddess's toes
The tatters of her once resplendent garment gleam garishly
Crumbling visage exposing clay and straw
One eye a hollowed sparrow's nest
Limbs coming askew
Standing abandoned
Having served her purpose of wish fulfillment
A forgotten plaything used and abused by empty devotion
Still she smiles benignly
The remaining eye wide and radiant
At the half-crazed tramp snoring at her feet below.

In Search of a New Home

MARZIA RAHMAN

Migration is tough, littered with blank memories and a bleak future. It's not something you ever hope to do.

Yet, you find yourself standing in a long queue, with a tiny bundle in hand, despairing to do or not to do? Fleeing a country that you naively thought yours. Stepping on a country that you know nothing about. That would never accept you as her own. Non-belonging is not a breezy concept, a topical topic in a critical theory. It's an unnerving parable of human condition that no human ever yearns for.

You shudder, clasping the tiny bundle, containing your entire household, your sixteen years of life. Behind you, in a burnt house of a burnt village, your parents, your very old grandmother and your two young siblings buried under the ideological beliefs of the state. Too complicated to grasp. Too easy to elude. "They don't want you," a clear and loud message the government sent to your people through army, arson, and atrocity.

Where is God? Your silly query swirls in the smoky air of a plundered village where dead people shrouded beneath dead humanity.

Tears fall on the tiny bundle, too small to carry so much misery. How can you leave your home where every dusty road is filled with memories, stories and songs? Where once a young man presented you a handwritten poem and a lotus flower. Where is he now? Dead or alive? Will he search for you?

The long queue gets smaller, some move forward, a few cries looking back at the village while boarding the boat.

Your turn.

They ask for money.

A gold chain, a few coins, a nose pin?

You have none.

Yet, the duo, one boatman and a middleman let you in. They have other means to usurp the debt.

You are crammed between a family with five children, an old woman with acne and a little boy with a broken toy. There are others, men, women, children— your people— hunched and twisted in a small, shabby boat in silence.

Hours after hours, you travel in an opaque night under a livid moon. The endless sea stretches endlessly. What is the name of the sea? No one knows. Your people are poor farmers, illiterate housewives. None of you have ever read history, geography or geology. Ever stood in front of the Taj Mahal or saw any of the seven wonders. You have no idea of its existence. How would you know the glow of the sea is called sea sparkle? How would you grasp that it's not magic but the phosphorescent waves lighting up the night?

Soon, you and your people would reach a new place. A new country with fresh troubles. Maybe, a new hell. Yet, each of you pray earnestly to reach there safely and soundly. You have no desire to be part of the global headlines. To be found lying face-down on some unknown beach.

All you want is a new home. To build new dream.

She Swam in the Yare

ALICE WILLITTS

                                    my grandmother
was an explorer's courtesan, swallowing
his rough gemstones like a human vault

                                  he bought her
siamese lizard skins, five wingless parakeets,
armfuls of pink figs, his ship's compass

                                          tattooed his chart on her
pristine skin so they both knew exactly where his fingers
had been until she mirrored all his blue archipelagoes
                                                till the day
her rainforest eyes folded and she opened herself to death
the way a mountain gives up its water
                                  weeping
                                        he flayed her
peeled the necromap from her flesh, shifty as a witness
and climbed into her skin, as if it were his own

Three Times Two, a Balloon for You

MEGHOMALA BHATTACHARYA

Six year old Nila counts two metal coins
and her eyes are too big
on her blackened charcoal face.

Outside Oly Pub this morning
a woman's silk saree smacking of lavender
brushes her hair and she follows it down Park Street.

Nila slows down as the lavender is lost;
she smells beer and cinnamoned tobacco
as one after another the bars release afterlives...

and she memorizes neon alphabets on flashing signboards.
The beeri-seller who sits outside the abandoned red-and-yellow post office,
once told her they're English words;
Six year old Nila counts, ek, do, teen, chaar...
All in all she has sixteen numbers for sixteen eateries her tummy wants.

All in all she has two metal coins and seven balloons to sell,
So she walks down Park Street and her bare feet pause
and drag her back and forth on the pavements outside
the sugary bakery Flury's
and the roasted lamb at Barbeque Nation,
and the melting cheese at Mocambo's;

Six year old Nila sells a balloon to a six year old handsome boy,
whose mother tosses two coins at her
and she walks some more and arrives outside Quest Mall,
(the giant glass pyramid for those that toss her money)

and tosses her four coins at the jhaal-muri seller
and little Nila now has food and no more coins
and so she marches outside the restaurants with six balloons in her hands.

Old Love

NAINA DEY

I saw you last night
in a sudden dream
Was it a garden party
or an open-air show
You came with someone I didn't know
and didn't bother to like
I noticed you wore your curly hair long
Tied at the back with a band
Fastened with clips
You had even aged somewhat
But smiled the same smile

I hid behind the chairs and flowerpots
My eyes following you among the bubbling crowd
For I didn't want you to see me
To raise your hand to say, "Hi!"
To shatter the magic of childhood infatuation
Of dissolving whispers and kisses
All I wanted was to taste you with my eyes
To love you with all your faults and your bad hairstyle
Made heady by the vintage of old love made new.

Reclusion

VIJAY KHURANA

1. You laughed at the joke but now you have stopped laughing. You have eased your laugh into a tight smile—so tight it is almost painful—and you are waiting for him to realise that the joke is over. You look at his trousers. They are not nice trousers, you think, smiling so tightly it is almost painful. He keeps sniffing laughter out in great chunks, as though he will never stop. You look at the corduroy, at the creases that bloom across the tops of his thighs. You are alone.

2. I was a hermit once. Only for a week. My boss said that instead of a raise or a bonus I could go and stay in his holiday house. I would have preferred the raise but I didn't argue. He drove me there in his silver Mercedes and promised to pick me up a week later. The nearest shop was miles away but he told me there was enough tinned food and spaghetti to keep me going. I ate smoked oysters from the tin and looked out the window at the mountains. By the fourth day I was having what you could call visions. They weren't exactly spiritual, or even creative. Egotistical, maybe. I was convinced that the low hum coming periodically from the fuse-box could be the cornerstone, the backbone, the coat-hook of an entire novel. I had three days to write it.

3. There are two main beers in Cambodia and one is Angkor and one is Anchor and Angkor is pronounced anchor and Anchor is pronounced Anne chore and I was always an anchorite.

(im)mortal

REBECCA PHILLIPS

a hint of gold in the blood lingers—hovers in the air as a crow
dances on telephone lines—they walk among us with their
voices hushed and their stature strong, taking us for lovers,
for friends, for victims. they watch our limbs weaken, touch
our hair as the colour fades, and vanish with a smile sharp as
steel before we venture where they cannot go.

others hide in the shadows, guiding a child one bore them.
the child pulled from the impact of an oncoming truck,
steered to smoke-free air to escape a cigarette fire, pushed
to the surface between waves ragged as the rocks they crash
against, does not know how they are kept alive, slipping from
death's greedy fingers where others would have choked.

their names, long ago, would tumble from feeble mouths in
desperation—please, have mercy on my daughter's life, give
my son the glory he so desires, kill the man who plans to take
my throne—

the gods still play their games, even if no one calls out to
them. they choose their favourites; those with a hole in their
heart that cannot be filled by mortal whims, but the spoils
to be won are no longer gold unfathomable or the bodies
of enemies. as humanity has grown and evolved, so has the
deepness of our wants.

the immortals remain stagnant as metal; what they seek
never wavers, they merely have to sift through generations of
men to get it. men do not have the pleasure of eternity.

we beg for things even gods cannot grant.

we beg even when we do not believe.

mortality is a fragile thing, and it makes you do fragile things.

I from Krakov, You from Nagasaki

KATARZYNA BIELA

we met accidentally as we were trying
to find our ways around the city
I from here
you from there
we decided the best way
would be to go straight together
the town still a stranger to us

we must be heading towards the centre
when we start a conversation
the street informs us
with huge white letters on the tough concrete
that we are about to pass a school
what they teach here we have no idea
so we amuse ourselves by talking about our homes

you say you know my country used not to exist
I say I know yours was once reduced to atoms
that's easy to remember
we don't need any revisions

the school is gone when we turn to complex things
I ask you to repeat your name several times
then try to pronounce it myself
spelling belongs to the second year syllabus I hope

no time for more the city centre sign
suggests we know where we are now
I go here
and you there

let's meet again one day
only not at night
though air bubbles going up towards the surface
of beer are beautiful

but let's not risk our curtains drawing unexpectedly
let's take it slow
let's feel we've got lots of time on our hands
fingertips are actually the only thing we can truly show
in this land strange but at least neutral

let's meet again and have a picnic
I might even learn what snacks you like
we'll find our own place on the concrete
and draw a hopscotch court

you tell me which square to jump on

Two Places Ago

SRISHTI DUTTA CHOWDHURY

I will drag the lake into this.
sometimes I don't find the right side to
bare my body to the
wind. speaking of lake, that predisposition with
hooks. the fishing kind, the wince at the end of the line bearing
a gash against the belly of the sea.
the shard of pink flesh eating at
my mouth. my mouth. I am
feasting on the horror of scales. foisting oil over
the silver, fostering the cave of dark teeth, the
mound of eye with this fork.
I will drag the mouth that wilts like
a wildflower over the wound of this. like the palmy, carmine of
canna. your mouth weighs a thousand
lies on scales. the right place for
a wrinkled laughter. the setting sun. this blouse
of mauve sticking gum on
flesh. your tongue scouring the ridges against
glass. the window of the lake. the slick pat of wind over the crest heaving
out of water.

over and over, I lower the
hearse. you will not stay

This is a Letter to Whoever is Next

ALICE WILLITTS

Be the red crab-apple winter with green-faced snowflakes. Be the polished reflections of pansy faces; their collection of giggling. Never a white brick, alone. Lean white. Be a small solid thing in a line of sisters ready to sprint off a runner's block. Be a dark-eyed sky-cutter with sufficient symmetry to spillikin the sky. A tree is a long wait rising. Pigeons ripple arches on the sluice gate; their weir tier trick. A lock is a long wait in reversing nature. Perhaps you'll be a jug of hedgehog milk while you wait?

Holy city. Tree-scarf city catching the wisdom of clouds. No matter, a scratch is a longing to repeat something lasting. Go up the river in darkening voices as a raft of numbers on the Cam or the Yare. Or stay chained. Be a chilly noose, a crimped river neatly lined. Be the plant with the milky sap that blisters skin in the sun. Remember each marked day is slanted in echoes of what is beyond its plain green lines. Seize D for day, yes, and duty; do your own bad damage; I do not care. I am so lovely still.

Be the pious berry pyre of eighty-three, the frontier of elderly, dipping its fingers in the font with two faces. A young face inside and the one that looks the other way. Be fingers pressing an old cheek that raises its slow memory up all morning. Alright, go on, be the stone font with two faces and look away while they drink the sparrow water.

Be red signs on faces puffing che-che-che round Castle Hill, up like a snail down like a swirl. Be the tax on menstruation. Be Janus, lord of the river beginnings, god of the wakeful whose ghost drives taxis through graffiti. Run backstreets, cut through time over yellow bridges and stop only for the pink tower. Tourists.

Remember three kisses is secret code for I hate you. The girls spell it out on the step's swirling leaf packets. They know how to jump their fendom. Be the flatness.

WRITING PLACES

First published by UEA Publishing Project 2019.
International ©2019 retained by individual authors.

Writing Places is typeset in Garamond with titles in Lydian
Cover Design by Anna Brewster © 2019.
Typeset by Anna Brewster.
Photography by Sarah Hickson

ISBN 9781911343943

Printed and bound in the UK by Imprint Digital Distributed by NBN International.